George Washington's Socks

Elvira Woodruff

STUDENT PACKET

NOTE:

The trade book edition of the novel used to prepare this guide is found in the Novel Units catalog and on the Novel Units website. Using other editions may have varied page references.

Please note: We have assigned Interest Levels based on our knowledge of the themes and ideas of the books included in the Novel Units sets, however, please assess the appropriateness of this novel or trade book for the age level and maturity of your students prior to reading with them. You know your students best!

BN 978-1-56137-087-0

To order, contact your
local school supply store, or:

Toll-Free Fax: 877.716.7272
Phone: 888.650.4224
3901 Union Blvd., Suite 155
St. Louis, MO 63115

sales@novelunits.com

novelunits.com

Preparing for Time Travel

Directions: Prepare for reading by answering the following short-answer questions.

1. Who is the author?

   _____

2. What does the title suggest to you about the book?

   _____

   _____

   _____

   _____

3. When was the book first copyrighted?

   _____

4. How many pages are there in the book?

   _____

5. Thumb through the book. Read three pages—one from near the beginning, one from near the middle, and one from near the end. What predictions can you make about the book?

   _____

   _____

   _____

   _____

6. What does the cover suggest to you about the book?

   _____

   _____

   _____

   _____

Sentence Starters

Directions: Use the sentence starters below to write one or two sentences about your opinions on the chosen topic. Use the lines below or a separate sheet of paper if you need more space.

1. Younger siblings should never

_____

_____

_____

2. Leadership is needed when…

_____

_____

_____

3. War is always…

_____

_____

_____

4. Time travel is dangerous because…

_____

_____

_____

5. An enemy can become a friend when…

_____

_____

_____

Name _____

Vocabulary Concentration

stole	suppress	desperate	smugly
rebel	bayonet	defeat	verge
abnormal	muster	charter	adventurous
array	arsenal		

Directions: Working with a partner, make two sets of cards. On one set, write each vocabulary word (one word per card). On the second set, write each vocabulary word's definition (one definition per card; only write on one side of the card).

Object of the Game: Match vocabulary words with their definitions by remembering each card's location.

Game Instructions: Shuffle both sets of cards together. Spread the cards face down on a table. Turn over two cards. If the cards match a vocabulary word with its definition, keep both cards and take another turn. If the cards don't match, return them to their places face down on the table. Your partner takes a turn. Continue playing until all cards have been matched correctly. The player with the most cards wins.

Name _____

Vocabulary Sentence Sets

legend	fantastic	canteen	batty
comrades	eerie	transfixed	hoisting
vessel	mistrust	trance	feeble
veered	abrupt	floes	paralyzed
console			

Directions: Write the vocabulary words on the numbered lines below.

1. _____   2. _____

3. _____   4. _____

5. _____   6. _____

7. _____   8. _____

9. _____   10. _____

11. _____   12. _____

13. _____   14. _____

15. _____   16. _____

17. _____

On a separate sheet of paper, use each of the following sets of words in an original sentence. Your sentences should show that you know the meanings of the vocabulary words as they are used in the story.

Sentence 1: words 8 and 4
Sentence 2: words 9 and 3
Sentence 3: words 1 and 10
Sentence 4: words 11 and 7
Sentence 5: words 15 and 13
Sentence 6: words 3 and 6
Sentence 7: words 12 and 4
Sentence 8: words 14 and 9
Sentence 9: words 5 and 2
Sentence 10: words 7 and 6
Sentence 11: words 16 and 4
Sentence 12: words 11 and 17

| © Novel Units, Inc.

Vocabulary Wheel

imposing	foe	muskets	foreign
perplexed	enlist	riveted	venture
resist	disembark	guardian	diverted
ensured	capacity	regiment	conceal
befell			

Directions: Write each vocabulary word on a piece of paper (one word per piece). Make a spinner using the circle below. Now play the following game with a classmate. (It is a good idea to have a dictionary and thesaurus handy.) Place the papers in a small container. Draw a word from the container. Then spin the spinner and follow the direction where the pointer lands. For example, if you draw the word "imposing" and land on "Define," you must define the word **imposing**. If your partner accepts the answer as correct, you score one point and play passes to your partner. If your partner challenges the answer, use a dictionary or thesaurus to prove the answer is correct. If you can prove the answer is correct, you earn two points. If you cannot prove the answer is correct, your partner earns two points. Play continues until all the words have been used. The player with the most points wins.

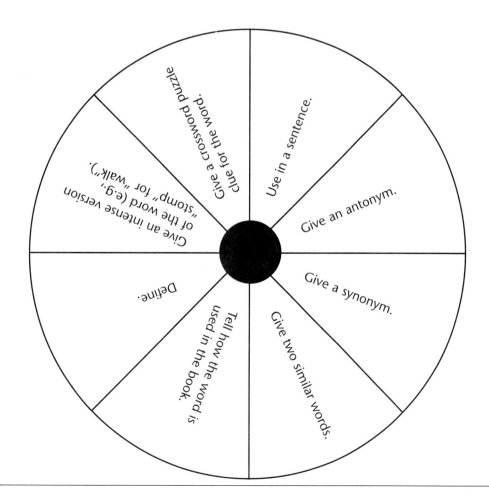

Name _____

Vocabulary Word Map

pry	haggard	vexed	ornate
scow	artillery	patriot	siege
expedite	chided	chapped	instill
scourge	rations	mature	

Directions: Choose seven words from the vocabulary list. Complete a word map for each word on separate sheets of paper. Use the word map below as an example.

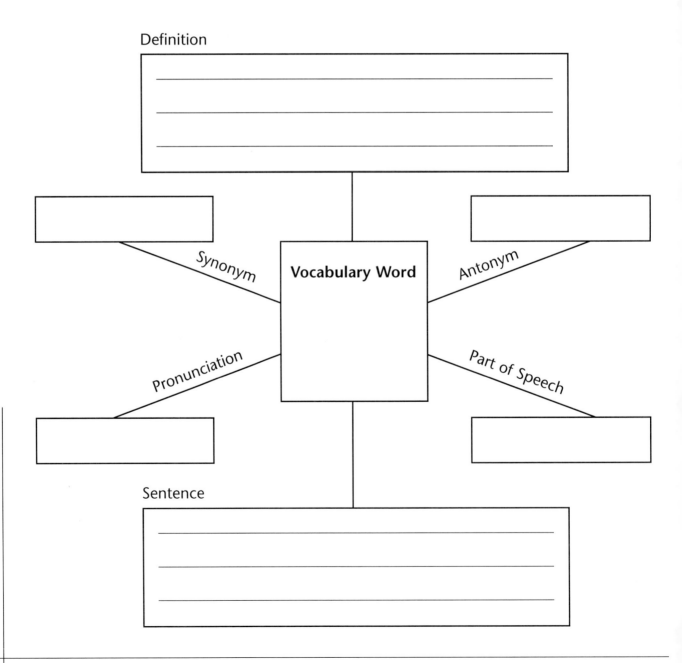

violently	phlegm	spasms	agony
brusque	enticing	encased	wriggling
savoring	garment	drab	militia
jittery	clearance	plundering	yonder
profound			

Directions: Each of the words below is either a synonym or an antonym of a vocabulary word. The first letter of the related vocabulary word appears after each word. Finish writing the related vocabulary word on the line. Circle the words that are synonyms, and underline those that are antonyms.

1. pleasing—e_____

2. seizures—s_____

3. enclosed—e_____

4. peacefully—v_____

5. twisting—w_____

6. suffering—a_____

7. calm—j_____

8. attire—g_____

9. authorization—c_____

10. disliking—s_____

11. army—m_____

12. shallow—p_____

13. looting—p_____

14. near—y_____

15. colorful—d_____

16. polite—b_____

17. mucus—p_____

Vocabulary Chart

embraced	calf	resumed	implored
crucial	terrain	gait	forging
warrior	ruddy	ambush	surrender

Directions: Write each vocabulary word in the left-hand column of the chart. Complete the chart by placing a check mark in the column that best describes your familiarity with each word. Working with a partner, find and read the line where each word appears in the story. Find the meaning of each word in the dictionary. Together with your partner, choose ten of the words checked in the last column. On a separate sheet of paper, use each of those words in a sentence.

Vocabulary Word	I Can Define	I Have Seen/Heard	New Word For Me

buck	severest	intent	diverted
slain	frisk	turncoats	stout
victorious	despite	vague	awestruck
solemnly			

Directions: Determine the meaning of the underlined vocabulary words, and answer the following questions.

1. Is a <u>buck</u> an adult male deer or an adult female deer?

2. Is the <u>severest</u> winter the mildest or harshest?

3. Is a <u>diverted</u> student sidetracked or satisfied?

4. You are <u>intent</u> on passing the test. Are you determined or distracted?

5. The dragon was <u>slain</u>. Was the dragon caged or killed?

6. When police <u>frisk</u> suspects, do they search or observe the suspects?

7. Are <u>turncoats</u> heroes or traitors?

8. Your friend is <u>stout</u>. Is he heavy or slim?

9. Is the <u>victorious</u> team the winner or loser?

10. You fail <u>despite</u> your effort. Do you fail because of your effort or regardless of your effort?

11. You are given <u>vague</u> directions. Are you clear or unclear on where you are going?

12. You are <u>awestruck</u>. Are you feeling wonder or weariness?

13. Someone speaks <u>solemnly</u>. Do they speak seriously or jokingly?

Name _____

dispel	anxiety	console	activate
encircled	depart	unruly	unraveled
chorus	utmost	antique	lush
divulge			

Directions: Write a summary of the novel. Use at least seven of the vocabulary words above in your summary. Start writing on the lines below, and continue on a separate sheet of paper if you need more space.

_____

_____

_____

_____

_____

_____

_____

_____

_____

_____

_____

_____

_____

_____

_____

_____

_____

_____

© Novel Units, Inc.

Directions: Answer the following questions on a separate sheet of paper. Use your answers in class discussions, for writing assignments, and to review for tests. Starred questions indicate thought or opinion questions.

Chapters One–Three

1. What does the Adventure Club read about at its first meeting?
2. Where does the first club meeting take place?
3. What makes Katie giggle during dinner?
4. How do Matt and Q know a lot about George Washington?
5. Why was George Washington discouraged before he crossed the river? What did he need?
6. *Why does Matt think Tony is an important member of the club? What does this tell you about Matt?
7. What is Q's full first name?
8. What is Hooter's real name? How did he get his nickname?
9. Why is Katie only a temporary club member?
10. What adventure does Matt suggest for the club?
11. How does Katie avoid being left behind by the boys?
12. Why is Q against taking Katie with them?

Chapters Four–Six

1. Who told Tony about the legend of the lake?
2. What is the lake's name? What did it used to be called?
3. Who is Adam Hibbs? What happened to him?
4. Why does Matt feel he must be the bravest?
5. What does Tony's grandfather tell Tony about the lake's name?
6. Why does Katie leave the boys?
7. Where does Matt find Katie?
8. What feelings does Matt have when he sees the boat?
9. How does Matt know something is wrong before he opens his eyes?
10. Who falls out of the boat?
11. Who comforts Matt?
12. What do Q and Tony find in the boat?

Name _____

Chapters Seven–Nine

1. Who rescues Katie from the ice floe?

2. Why doesn't Washington know where Nebraska is?

3. Who does Washington suspect Matt and his friends are?

4. What is the name of the river they cross?

5. Who mans the boats carrying Washington and his troops?

6. How many troops are ferried across the river?

7. Why do officers wear paper in their hats?

8. Who is assigned to watch over Matt and his friends? Why does this excite the boys? What worries Q?

9. Why does Matt leave his friends?

10. What happens to Corporal Hibbs?

11. What does Matt accidentally become?

Chapters Ten–Twelve

1. How far is the march to Trenton?

2. How is it possible to tell one regiment from another?

3. Why does Matt give one sneaker to Israel Gates?

4. What does Israel give Matt to eat?

5. Why did Israel join the army?

6. Why don't many shopkeepers accept Continental currency?

7. Why is Matt glad he did his history report?

8. Why did Colonel Henry Knox join the army?

9. *How do you know Matt and Israel are friends? Why do you think they become friends in such a short period of time?

10. If Washington's troops are defeated at Trenton, what will be lost?

11. What does Matt learn about drummers' uniforms?

12. Why is Matt suddenly afraid?

Chapters Thirteen–Fifteen

1. Why does Israel lean on Matt?
2. *What does Henry give Matt? What does this tell you about Henry?
3. What does Matt promise Israel?
4. Why does Matt tell Israel about Batman?
5. Who is Nathan Hornbee?
6. Of whom does Mrs. Hornbee remind Matt?
7. How does Henry save Matt's life?
8. What do the Hornbees say is too dangerous?
9. What about Matt's clothes interest the Hornbees?
10. What does Mrs. Hornbee give Matt?
11. What does Matt break? Why?

Chapters Sixteen–Eighteen

1. What does Matt do when he is afraid?
2. Who are with the two Indian boys?
3. Why was Adam Hibbs glad to see the Adventure Club?
4. Where did the soldiers hide the rowboat?
5. *Why do you think Tony takes so long to tell Matt about Katie and Q?
6. Who carried Katie and Q away on their shoulders?
7. Why does Matt think the Indians know where the Hessians are?
8. How does the Indian react to Tony's video game? Why does he react this way?
9. Why do the Hessians look like giants?
10. What does Q have that the Hessians like? What does he have that angers them?
11. *Do you think Matt's plan to rescue Q and Katie is a good plan? Why or why not?

Chapters Nineteen–Twenty

1. What does the Adventure Club do when the Hessians wave their swords and shout?

2. Why is Matt glad the redheaded soldier isn't guarding them?

3. What might control the rowboat?

4. Why does King George pay the Hessians to fight?

5. Who makes friends with Gustav?

6. What happens to Katie when she spots a baby duck?

7. Why doesn't Matt thank Gustav?

8. What worries Matt when the rebel soldiers examine Tony's dollar bill?

9. When did the soldier find Israel's beads?

10. What does George Washington give Katie? What does he promise Matt?

11. What do Matt and Hooter hate?

Chapters Twenty-one–Twenty-three

1. What does Katie know that the others do not?

2. What does the Adventure Club learn about "Emit Levart"?

3. What is wrong with the rowboat?

4. What powers the rowboat?

5. How does Matt determine where they are?

6. *How will Matt explain his lost sneakers to his parents?

7. What will Matt miss about the 18th century?

8. Why can't Katie keep Washington's socks? What is her solution?

9. What do Hooter, Tony, and Q plan to do when they get home?

10. How do the Adventure Club members react when Matt talks about using the rowboat for future adventures?

11. What does Matt do when he gets home? Why?

12. Why is Mr. Carlton proud of Matt?

Name _____

Directions: For each letter of the alphabet, write a word that relates to George Washington. Words can describe his character, his actions in the novel, or information about him you have researched. Put a star next to words that can also be used to describe Matt.

A _____   Q _____

B _____   R _____

C _____   S _____

D _____   T _____

E _____   U _____

F _____   V _____

G _____   W _____

H _____   X _____

I _____   Y _____

J _____   Z _____

K _____

L _____

M _____

N _____

O _____

P _____

Character Analysis

Directions: Working in small groups, discuss the attributes of the various characters. In each character's box, write several words or phrases that describe him or her.

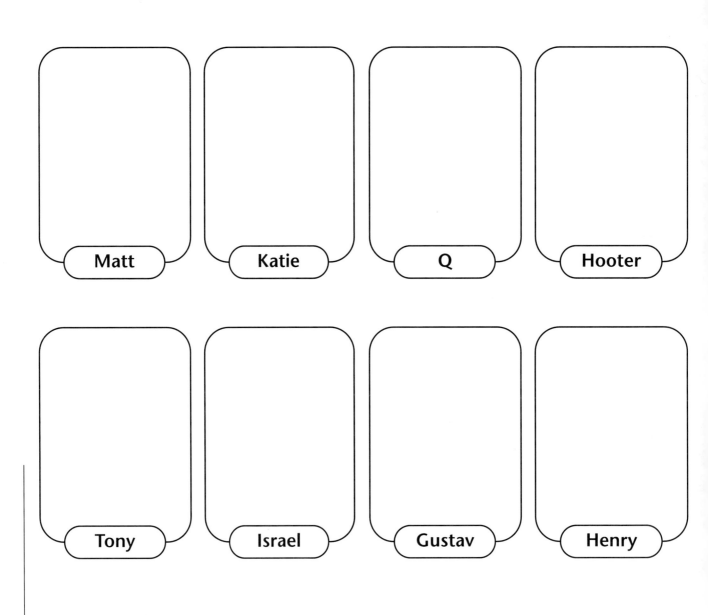

Matt

Katie

Q

Hooter

Tony

Israel

Gustav

Henry

Name _____

A Character's World

Directions: You may be able to draw parallels between a character's world and your own. Write a character's name in the blank. Describe that character's world. Then describe a related situation or event from your own world.

_____'s World

_____
_____
_____

My World

_____
_____

_____'s World

_____
_____
_____

My World

_____
_____

_____'s World

_____
_____
_____

My World

_____
_____

_____'s World

_____
_____
_____

My World

_____
_____

Solving Problems

Directions: List six problems the characters in the novel face. Then complete the rest of the chart. For each problem, circle which solution you think is best—yours or the character's.

Problem	Character's Solution	Your Solution

Name _____

Fact and Opinion

A fact is information that can be proven. An opinion is a personal viewpoint.

Directions: Read the following sentences. Write an F if the statement is a fact. Write an O if the statement is an opinion.

_____ 1. The legend of Lake Levart is frightening.

_____ 2. George Washington is the leader of the Continental Troops.

_____ 3. The enemy uses cowardly tactics.

_____ 4. Washington's officers wear paper in their hats so the soldiers can recognize them in the dark.

_____ 5. Being a rebel soldier in the Revolutionary War is a nightmare.

_____ 6. Hessian soldiers are giants.

_____ 7. There is no such thing as good guys fighting bad guys.

_____ 8. "Emit Levart" spelled backwards is time travel.

_____ 9. It's good to live in the twentieth century.

_____ 10. Hessian soldiers are from Germany.

Bonus: In the space below, rewrite one of the above opinions to make it a fact.

Directions: In the box below, draw a picture or symbol of what you think is the most important part of the story. Explain your picture or symbol on the lines below.

_____
_____
_____
_____
_____
_____

Name _____

Story Map

Directions: Fill in the story map below.

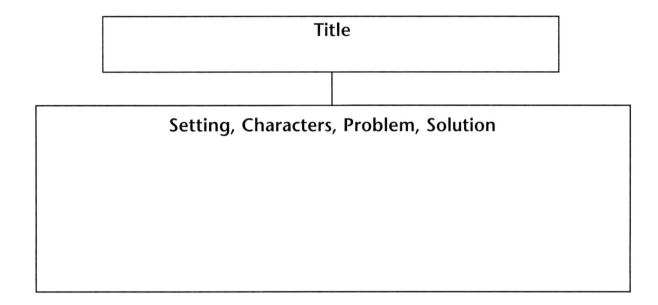

Series of Events

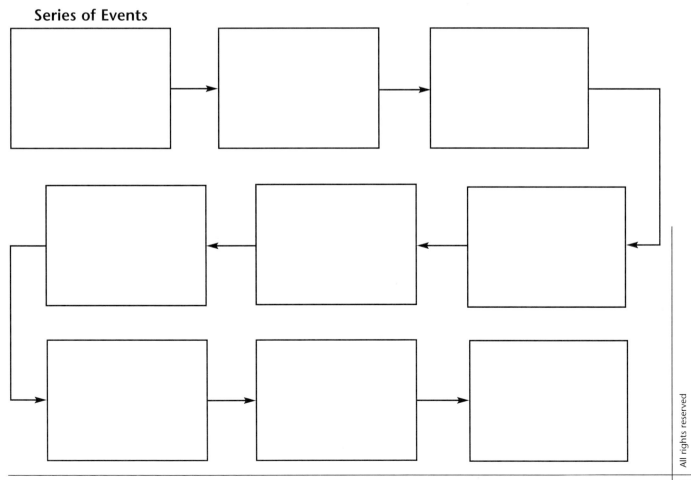

Name _____

Directions: Create an advertisement for a new Adventure Club member. List specific skills that the new member should have based on the needs of the club and the skills some members already have.

The Nebraska Times

Wednesday, October 2 • Section A, Page 1

_____

_____

_____

_____

_____

_____

_____

_____

_____

_____

_____

_____

_____

_____

_____

Directions: Write another time-travel adventure featuring the Adventure Club. Include a new club member in your story. Continue your story on a separate sheet of paper.

_____

_____

_____

_____

_____

_____

_____

_____

_____

_____

_____

_____

_____

_____

_____

_____

_____

_____

_____

_____

_____

_____

_____

_____

Name _____

A. Fill in the Blanks

1. George Washington's crossing of the Delaware River happens in the winter of

   _____.

2. In the Adventure Club, Matt is the _____, Tony is the

   _____, Q is the _____, and Hooter is the

   _____ _____.

3. All of the people who disappeared from Lake Levart were in a _____.

4. _____ _____ pulls Katie off an ice floe.

5. Matt is handed a musket when he returns Washington's _____.

6. Many battles would have been lost without Henry Knox and his _____.

7. The _____ works for and against Washington and his troops.

8. The soldiers are fighting to rid the colonies of the rule of King _____.

9. Israel describes the Hessians as _____.

10. _____ wear the colors of their regiment, only reversed.

B. Short Answer: Write your answer on the lines below.

11. What forces George Washington to cross the Delaware River in winter?

   _____

   _____

   _____

   _____

   _____

   _____

   _____

   _____

Name _____

A. True/False

_____ 1. Henry wants Matt to stay with Israel.

_____ 2. Matt leaves the beads at Mr. Hornbee's farm.

_____ 3. Indians guide Matt, Tony, and Hooter to Q and Katie in exchange for a video game and shoe buckles.

_____ 4. Gustav rescues Katie from the old rowboat.

_____ 5. Washington's troops win the battle at Trenton.

_____ 6. Matt regrets not thanking Gustav for saving Katie's life.

_____ 7. The mind can activate the rowboat's power.

_____ 8. Matt will miss the eighteenth century.

_____ 9. Katie trades Washington's socks for a bag of candy.

_____ 10. Katie is good at keeping secrets.

B. Short Answer: Write your answer on the lines below.

11. What does Matt learn from Gustav?

_____

_____

_____

_____

_____

_____

Name _____

A. Matching: Match each character with the correct description.

____ 1. Matt

____ 2. Katie

____ 3. Tony

____ 4. Q

____ 5. Hooter

____ 6. Gustav

____ 7. Adam Hibbs

____ 8. Israel Gates

____ 9. Henry Schudder

____ 10. Nathan Hornbee

a. 13-year-old drummer

b. Adventure Club's brain

c. patriot farmer

d. Adventure Club's strong man

e. Hessian soldier

f. rebel soldier

g. Adventure Club's president

h. time traveler's grandson

i. Adventure Club's scout

j. Adventure Club's associate vice president

B. Identification: Explain how each word is important to the story. Write one or two sentences for each word.

11. boats

_____

_____

12. shoes

_____

_____

13. socks

_____

_____

14. beads

_____

_____

15. dollars

_____

_____

© Novel Units, Inc.

Name _____

C. Multiple Choice: Choose the BEST answer.

_____ 16. Disappearances on the lake happen when there is a
    (a) full moon
    (b) new moon
    (c) one-quarter moon
    (d) three-quarter moon

_____ 17. George Washington and 2,400 troops crossed the Delaware River in
    (a) 1676
    (b) 1776
    (c) 1876
    (d) 1976

_____ 18. Washington's troops march nine miles to
    (a) New York, New York
    (b) Philadelphia, Pennsylvania
    (c) Rumson, Nebraska
    (d) Trenton, New Jersey

_____ 19. Israel Gates joins the army to
    (a) become a man
    (b) buy beads for Abby
    (c) fight for his independence
    (d) feed his sister and brothers

_____ 20. Tony and Hooter leave Q and Katie with
    (a) Adam Hibbs
    (b) the Hessians
    (c) the Indians
    (d) the rowboat

_____ 21. Matt knows about video games, but the Indian boys know about
    (a) guns
    (b) shoe buckles
    (c) survival
    (d) Washington's plans

Name _____

_____ 22. The Hessians came to America to fight because
   (a) Washington paid them
   (b) King George paid them
   (c) King George begged them
   (d) they wanted to immigrate to America

_____ 23. George Washington promises Matt that he will
   (a) find the rowboat
   (b) give his socks to Katie
   (c) get the beads to Israel's sister
   (d) punish the soldiers for shooting Gustav

_____ 24. Hooter and Matt hate
   (a) eating pigeon
   (b) following orders
   (c) time travel
   (d) war

_____ 25. Q will keep Washington's socks in
   (a) his bedroom closet
   (b) his locker at school
   (c) the bottom of the rowboat
   (d) a frame above his snakeskin collection

_____ 26. Katie tells her parents about
   (a) Gustav rescuing her
   (b) the peas in the sugar bowl
   (c) crossing the Delaware River
   (d) General George Washington

_____ 27. Which of the following is NOT one of Matt's traits?
   (a) courage
   (b) fear
   (c) kindness
   (d) pretty

D. Essay: Select I or II, and write your response on the lines below.

I. How is leadership important to the story? Use information from the book to support your answer.

II. How is friendship important to the story? Use information from the book to support your answer.

_____

_____

_____

_____

_____

_____

_____

_____

_____

_____

_____

_____

_____

_____

_____

_____

_____

_____

_____

_____

_____

_____

E. Creative Writing: Select one of the essay options below, and write your response on a separate sheet of paper.

I. Write a letter to George Washington telling him what freedom means to you. Include your thoughts about his leadership abilities and his troops' courage.

II. Write a story about the members of the Adventure Club that takes place ten years in the future. Tell what Matt, Q, Tony, Hooter, and Katie are doing.

III. Write a letter to Matt and the Adventure Club offering advice about where and when to travel next and why.

IV. Write an interview between Matt and George Washington. Be sure to write both the questions Matt or George Washington might ask the other as well as their responses.

Answer Key

Activity #1: 1. Elvira Woodruff 2. Answers will vary. Example: The book is an adventure story about five kids who go back in time to the Revolutionary War. 3. 1991 4. 166. 5. Answers will vary. 6. Answers will vary.

Activity #2: Sentences will vary.

Activity #3: The player with the most cards wins.

Activity #4: Sentences will vary.

Activity #5: The player with the most points wins.

Activity #6: Maps will vary depending on words chosen.

Activity #7: 1. enticing 2. spasms 3. encased 4. violently 5. wriggling 6. agony 7. jittery 8. garment 9. clearance 10. savoring 11. militia 12. profound 13. plundering 14. yonder 15. drab 16. brusque 17. phlegm; Synonyms: 1, 2, 3, 5, 6, 8, 9, 11, 13, 17; Antonyms: 4, 7, 10, 12, 14, 15, 16

Activity #8: Answers will vary.

Activity #9: 1. adult male deer 2. harshest 3. sidetracked 4. determined 5. killed 6. search 7. traitors 8. heavy 9. winner 10. regardless 11. unclear 12. wonder 13. seriously

Activity #10: Summaries will vary.

Study Guide

Chapters One–Three: 1. the crossing of the Delaware River by George Washington and his army during the Revolutionary War 2. Tony's backyard 3. Matt hides his peas in the sugar bowl. 4. They worked together on a history report about Washington. 5. The American Army was on the verge of collapse; food, supplies, and a victory 6. Because Tony is small, he can be a scout; Answers will vary, but should include that Matt is kind because he makes Tony feel good about himself. 7. Quentin 8. Brian Melrose; from hooting at an injured baby owl he had found and cared for 9. The club's charter doesn't allow female members. 10. hiking to the lake 11. She threatens to tell on them. 12. Katie might fall in the lake or get lost.

Chapters Four–Six: 1. Tony's grandfather 2. Levy Lake; Lake Levart 3. a friend of Tony's grandfather; Adam disappeared on the lake. 4. He is the leader and president of the club. 5. It's a clue to the mystery. 6. She drops her marshmallows. 7. waiting for the rowboat, which she boards 8. compelled to board the boat, afraid of the boat and for Katie's safety, wants to save Katie 9. The quietness of the lake is replaced by a roaring river, and Matt is cold. 10. Katie 11. Hooter 12. an inscription that reads Emit Levart

Chapters Seven–Nine: 1. George Washington 2. Nebraska wasn't a state in 1776. 3. Tory runners 4. Delaware River 5. John Glover's Marbleheaders 6. 2,400 7. so the men can recognize them in the dark 8. Adam Hibbs; If Adam is the missing friend of Tony's grandfather, he may know how the Adventure Club can get home; Q wonders why Adam is still in the past. 9. to return Washington's cape 10. He falls on his bayonet. 11. a rebel soldier in the Revolutionary War

Chapters Ten–Twelve: 1. nine miles 2. Colonies have separate styles of dress; each regiment wears a different color shirt. 3. Israel Gates has a long, infected gash on his foot. 4. pigeon 5. to support his family 6. Shopkeepers don't believe the currency is worth anything. 7. Matt would not know where he is otherwise. 8. Knox is a patriot and didn't want his country to exist under King George's unfair rule. 9. Answers will vary. Suggestions: They help and tease each other; depending on someone during a difficult time often creates friendship, and no one likes being alone in frightening situations. 10. Philadelphia 11. The drummer's colors are reversed from the rest of the company so officers can spot them in a crowd of soldiers. 12. He could become a casualty in the battle at Trenton.

Chapters Thirteen–Fifteen: 1. Israel can barely stand, he grows weaker with each step, and weaves when he walks. 2. the wool strips wrapped around his hands; Answers will vary but should include that although Henry acts tough, he is a caring person. 3. to get the beads to Abby 4. to help Israel stay awake 5. a farmer who rescues Matt from the freezing cold 6. Mrs. Pritchet 7. Henry tells Mr. Hornbee where to look for Matt and asks him to help Matt. 8. talk about being a patriot and sheltering Matt 9. the zipper and stitches on Matt's jeans and the material of his sneaker 10. wool socks and a pair of shoes 11. his promise to Israel because he loses the beads

Chapters Sixteen–Eighteen: 1. closes his eyes 2. Hooter and Tony 3. He knew that his grandfather was telling the truth. 4. in the bushes 5. Answers will vary. Suggestions: Tony is afraid of Matt's reaction; he wants Matt to know the whole story first. 6. the Hessians 7. The Indians know a lot about the woods. 8. afraid; The Indian has never seen anything like it and thinks magic trapped a little man inside the box. 9. Their hats are two feet tall. 10. bubble gum; a dollar bill 11. Answers will vary.

Chapters Nineteen–Twenty: 1. surrender 2. The soldier looks mean. 3. something about the "mind" 4. The king is running out of British troops. 5. Hooter 6. Katie's leg falls through the ice. 7. Matt is too embarrassed about referring to Gustav as the enemy. 8. that they will notice the date 9. on the march back 10. his extra pair of socks; to get the beads to Israel's sister 11. war

Chapters Twenty-one–Twenty-three: 1. where the rowboat is 2. The inscription spelled backwards reads "time travel." 3. The boat's spell isn't pulling the Adventure Club as it did before. 4. a person's thoughts 5. Matt finds a potato chip bag floating in the lake and sees Tony's house. 6. Answers will vary. 7. the woods and the unspoiled landscape 8. The Adventure Club could get in trouble if parents find out about the socks; Katie trades the socks for a bag of marshmallows. 9. Hooter wants to eat; Tony wants a bath and clean clothes; Q is going to frame Washington's socks. 10. They don't like the idea at first, but later they remember things they liked about the adventure. 11. turns on every electric appliance; Answers will vary but should include that Matt appreciates the comforts of his time. 12. Including Katie on the campout shows Matt is becoming a mature, responsible person.

Activities #11–14: Answers will vary.

Activity #15: 1. O 2. F 3. O 4. F 5. O 6. O 7. O 8. F 9. O 10. F Bonus: Answers will vary.

Activities #16–19: Answers will vary.

Quiz #1: A. 1. 1776 2. president; scout; brain; strong man 3. rowboat 4. George Washington 5. cape 6. artillery 7. storm 8. George 9. giants 10. Drummers **B.** 11. Answers will vary. Example: Washington needs a victory to turn the tide in his favor. The rebel army is suffering losses, and many fear the American cause will be lost. The rebels need food and supplies. Because the Hessian troops will be tired after celebrating Christmas, Washington moves his troops into action, desperate for a victory to help reverse the fortunes of the American Army.

Quiz #2: A. 1. F 2. F 3. T 4. F 5. T 6. T 7. T 8. T 9. F 10. F **B.** 11. Answers will vary. Examples: Matt learns there are good and bad soldiers on both sides and that he hates war. Matt sees Gustav's bravery and realizes his mistake of not thanking Gustav.

Novel Test: A. 1. g 2. j 3. i 4. b 5. d 6. e 7. h 8. f 9. a 10. c **B.** Answers will vary. Examples: 11. The rowboat takes the Adventure Club back in time. Boats ferry Washington's troops across the Delaware River. 12. Many soldiers march barefoot. Israel needs Matt's sneaker to protect his injured foot. Matt's sneaker amazes Mr. Hornbee. As a gesture of kindness, Mrs. Hornbee gives Matt a pair of shoes, which he treasures. Matt's sneakers remain in the 18th century while Mrs. Hornbee's shoes travel to the 20th century. 13. Matt realizes his life is luxurious because he can refuse to wear a sock because it has stripes. Washington gives Katie his socks to keep her warm. Q insists that Washington's socks be treated with reverence. Katie trades Washington's socks for a bag of marshmallows. 14. To Israel, the beads are a gift; they represent family and better times. To Matt, the beads represent his promise to and friendship with Israel. Matt discusses the beads with Washington, and Washington shows his gratitude to Matt by promising to bring the beads to Abby. 15. Money doesn't impress the Indians. The Hessians think Q is a rebel when they see his dollar bill. Rebel soldiers are puzzled by Washington's picture on unfamiliar currency, and Matt worries that they will notice the strange date on the bill. **C.** 16. d 17. b 18. d 19. d 20. b 21. c 22. b 23. c 24. d 25. d 26. d 27. d **D.** Answers will vary. Refer to the scoring rubric on page 36 of this guide. **E.** Answers will vary. Refer to the scoring rubric on page 36 of this guide.

Linking Novel Units® Student Packets to National and State Reading Assessments

During the past several years, an increasing number of students have faced some form of state-mandated competency testing in reading. Many states now administer state-developed assessments to measure the skills and knowledge emphasized in their particular reading curriculum. This Novel Units® guide includes open-ended comprehension questions that correlate with state-mandated reading assessments. The rubric below provides important information for evaluating responses to open-ended comprehension questions. Teachers may also use scoring rubrics provided for their own state's competency test.

Scoring Rubric for Open-Ended Items

3-Exemplary	Thorough, complete ideas/information Clear organization throughout Logical reasoning/conclusions Thorough understanding of reading task Accurate, complete response
2-Sufficient	Many relevant ideas/pieces of information Clear organization throughout most of response Minor problems in logical reasoning/conclusions General understanding of reading task Generally accurate and complete response
1-Partially Sufficient	Minimally relevant ideas/information Obvious gaps in organization Obvious problems in logical reasoning/conclusions Minimal understanding of reading task Inaccuracies/incomplete response
0-Insufficient	Irrelevant ideas/information No coherent organization Major problems in logical reasoning/conclusions Little or no understanding of reading task Generally inaccurate/incomplete response